Biology 2a — Cells, Organs and Populations

Page 1 — Cells

Q1 a)   Plant, animal
  b)   cell wall
  c)   Both plant and animal cells, proteins
  d)   membrane
Q2 a)   The **nucleus** contains genetic material / chromosomes / genes / DNA. Its function is controlling the cell's activities.
  b)   **Chloroplasts** contain chlorophyll. Their function is to make food by photosynthesis.
  c)   The **cell wall** is made of cellulose. Its function is to support the cell and strengthen it.
Q3 a)   animal
  b)   E.g.

  c)   Respiration happens inside mitochondria, which provides energy for life processes.
Q4 a)   cell wall
  b)   cell membrane
  c)   cytoplasm
  d)   Because the genetic material is floating in the cytoplasm and not in a nucleus.

Pages 2-3 — Diffusion

Q1   random, higher, lower, net, bigger, gases
Q2 a)

  (The dye particles will have spread out evenly.)
  b)   The rate of diffusion would **speed up**.
  c)   The dye particles will move from an area of higher concentration (the drop of dye) to an area of lower concentration (the water).
Q3 a)   Switching a fan on will spread the curry particles more quickly through the house.
  b)   The curry will smell stronger. Adding more curry powder increases the concentration of the curry particles and increases the rate of diffusion of the curry particles to the air.
Q4 a)   False
  b)   False
  c)   True
  d)   True
  e)   False
Q5 a)   B
  b)   There is a greater concentration difference between the two sides of the membrane in model B so the molecules will diffuse faster.
Q6 a)   glucose
  b)   Starch molecules are too large to fit through the pores in the membrane, but the small glucose molecules would diffuse through to the area of lower glucose concentration outside the bag.

Page 4 — Specialised Cells

Q1 a)   red blood cells
  b)   sperm cell
  c)   guard cells
  d)   egg cell / ovum

Q2   Lots of chlor
  Tall shape... gives a large surface a...
  Thin shape... means you can pack more cells in at the top of the leaf.
Q3   stomata, turgid, photosynthesis, flaccid, night.
Q4 a)   Concave discs / biconcave discs
  b)   It gives them a large surface area for absorbing oxygen.
  c)   To leave even more room for haemoglobin / carrying oxygen.
Q5 a)   Sperm
  b)   Sperm
  c)   Egg
  d)   Sperm
  e)   Sperm

Pages 5-6 — Cell Organisation

Q1

Cell	Tissue	Organ	Organ System	Organism
sperm egg (human) white blood cell	blood muscle	stomach eye heart liver small intestine	digestive system reproductive system excretory system	snail cat dog

Q2 a)   True
  b)   False
  c)   True
  d)   True
  e)   True
  f)   False
  g)   True
Q3   epithelial cells, epithelial tissue, stomach, digestive system, human
Q4 a)   materials, nutrients, bile, organs, liver, tissues, muscular tissue, churn
  b)   It makes digestive juices that digest food.
  c)   E.g. pancreas, salivary glands.
Q5 a)   To exchange and transport materials.
  b)   The process by which cells become specialised for a particular job.
Q6 a)   A group of similar cells that work together to carry out a particular function.
  b)   A group of different tissues that work together to perform a certain function.
  c)   A group of organs working together to perform a particular function.

Pages 7-8 — Plant Structure and Photosynthesis

Q1   water + carbon dioxide → glucose + oxygen
Q2 a)   E.g. stems, roots, leaves
  b)   Mesophyll tissue — it's where most of the photosynthesis in a plant occurs.
  Epidermal tissue — it covers the whole plant.
  Xylem and phloem — it transports water, mineral ions and sucrose around the plant.
Q3 a)   00.00 (midnight)
  b)   There's no light at night so photosynthesis won't occur.
  c)   Plants use the food / glucose (from photosynthesis) they have stored during the day.
  d)

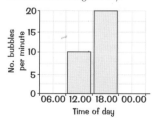

Q4 a) i)   Gas A = carbon dioxide
  Gas B = oxygen

Biology 2a — Cells, Organs and Populations

ii) As it gets lighter, the level of oxygen should increase as the plant will photosynthesise more and produce more oxygen. Carbon dioxide levels should decrease as light intensity increases, because the plant uses up carbon dioxide in photosynthesis.

b) i) As light intensity increases, the amount of carbon dioxide decreases.

ii) As light intensity increases, the amount of oxygen increases.

Q5 a) Plant B

b) The plant in the dark can't photosynthesise and so only has stored starch. The plant in sunlight is able to carry out photosynthesis and produce more glucose, which is then changed to more starch and stored in the leaves.

c) In the chloroplasts.

Pages 9-11 — The Rate of Photosynthesis

Q1 a) E.g. light intensity, CO_2 concentration, temperature

b) A factor that stops photosynthesis from happening any faster.

c) E.g. time of day (such as night time) / position of plant (such as in the shade).

Q2 a) It increases the rate of photosynthesis up to a certain point.

b) The rate of photosynthesis does not continue to increase because temperature or levels of carbon dioxide act as limiting factors.

Q3 a) blue light (approx. 440 nm), red light (approx. 660 nm)

b) You could use blue or red light bulbs to increase the rate of photosynthesis, and therefore the growth rate.

Q4 So that his plants grow well but so that he's not giving them more CO_2 than they need, as this would be wasting money.

Q5 a) the rate of photosynthesis

b)

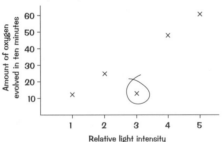

c) i) See circled point on graph.

ii) E.g. she might have collected the gas for less time than 10 minutes. / She might have accidentally used a lower light intensity. / She might have misread the syringe.

d) The rate of photosynthesis increased as light intensity increased.

e) The relationship would continue up to a point, and then the graph would level off. At this point, either the temperature or carbon dioxide level would be acting as a limiting factor.

Q6 a) amount of light and temperature

b) The faster the rate of photosynthesis, the faster the growth rate of the grass.

Q7 a) Any three from, e.g: it traps heat to make sure temperature does not become a limiting factor. / Artificial light can be used to enable photosynthesis to occur at all times. / Carbon dioxide can be maintained at a high level. / Plants can be kept free from pests. / Fertilisers can be added to provide all the necessary minerals for healthy plant growth.

b) i) a heater / artificial light / insulation

ii) ventilation or shades

iii) artificial lights

iv) To produce carbon dioxide and so increase carbon dioxide levels in the greenhouse, thus increasing the rate of photosynthesis.

Q8 a)

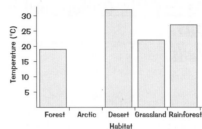

b) Arctic

c) The temperatures are extremely low there, so the rate of photosynthesis will be slower because the enzymes needed for photosynthesis will be working very slowly.

d) Despite the high temperatures, few plants grow in the desert because there is not enough water for them to survive.

Page 12 — How Plants Use Glucose

Q1 leaves, energy, convert, cells, cellulose, walls, lipids, margarine, cooking oil / cooking oil, margarine

Q2 a) nitrate ions

b) dhal — approx. 67%
steak — approx. 64%

c) Dhal, as it contains significantly more B vitamins, calcium and iron, than steak.

d) from plants

Q3 a) They change starch to glucose and use it for respiration to release energy for growth.

b) They use their leaves to make glucose by photosynthesis.

c) They store starch, which is insoluble, so they don't draw in loads of water and swell up as they would if they stored glucose.

Page 13 — Distribution of Organisms

Q1 a) True

b) False

c) True

Q2 Any three from, e.g: temperature / availability of water / availability of oxygen and carbon dioxide / availability of nutrients / amount of light.

Q3 a) A square frame enclosing a known area.

b) E.g. he could divide the field into a grid and use a random number generator to pick coordinates.

c) i) $(3 + 1 + 2 + 1 + 4 + 3 + 0 + 2) \div 8 = 2$ daisies per quadrat

ii) 0,1,1,2,2,3,3,4 so middle value (median) is 2

d) 5 600 x 2 = ·11 200 daisies

Page 14 — More on the Distribution of Organisms

Q1 a) i) E.g.

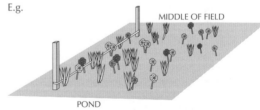

ii) E.g. she could collect data along the line by counting all the buttercups that touch it.

b) E.g. by having a larger sample size.

c) i) The number of buttercups decreases as you go further away from the pond.

ii) E.g. there is more water in the soil nearest to the pond, so more buttercups will grow there.

Q2 Bill's data isn't valid as it doesn't answer his question. The distribution of the dandelions could also be affected by the different soil moisture levels caused by the stream near the wood — he hasn't controlled all the variables.

GCSE

Additional Science

Exam Board: AQA

Answer Book

Higher Level

Contents

Published by CGP

ISBN: 978 1 84762 761 2

Printed by Elanders Ltd, Newcastle upon Tyne.
Clipart from Corel®

Based on the classic CGP style created by Richard Parsons.

Biology 2b — Enzymes and Genetics

Pages 15-17 — Mixed Questions — Biology 2a

Q1   Tissue — A group of similar cells that work together to carry out a certain function.
Diffusion — The spreading out of particles from an area of high concentration to an area of low concentration.
Habitat — The place where an organism lives.
Mode — The most common value in a set of data.
Photosynthesis — The process that produces 'food' (glucose) in plants and algae.
Limiting factor — Something that stops photosynthesis from happening any faster.
Differentiation — The process by which cells become specialised for a particular job.

Q2 a)   chloroplasts, vacuole, cell wall
b) i)

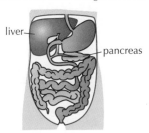

cell wall — nucleus
mitochondria — cytoplasm
vacuole — cell membrane
ribosome — chloroplast

ii)   chloroplasts / tall shape
Chloroplasts: contain chlorophyll for photosynthesis.
Tall shape: allows more palisade cells to be packed at the top of the leaf, and increases the surface area down the side of the cells for absorption of carbon dioxide / gaseous exchange.

Q3 a)   chlorophyll
b)   carbon dioxide, water
c) i)   starch
ii)   E.g. roots / stems / leaves
d)   For respiration, for making proteins, for making cell walls.

Q4 a) i)   mitochondria
ii)   cytoplasm
b)   It contracts (shortens) to move whatever it's attached to.
c) i)   To digest food. / To absorb soluble food molecules.
ii)   To absorb water from undigested food.
d) i) and ii)

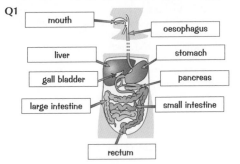

liver — pancreas

Q5 a)   diffusion
b)   Z particles are larger than X and Y particles.
c)   Protein solution, because protein molecules are bigger than amino acid or glucose molecules.
Q6 a)   A quadrat.
b)   Total area = 250 m x 180 m = 45 000 m²
Total area x number of plants = population
45 000 m² x 11 = **495 000**, so there's likely to be approximately 500 000 clover plants.
c) i)   (11 + 9 + 8 + 9 + 7) ÷ 5 = 8.8 plants
ii)   (It is the same field, so use 45 000 m² again.)
45 000 m² x 8.8 = 396 000 clover plants (≈ 400 000).
d)   Lisa's result is likely to be more accurate as she has used a larger sample size.

Biology 2b — Enzymes and Genetics

Pages 18-19 — Enzymes

Q1 a)   Enzymes are biological catalysts.

b)

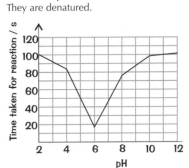

enzyme — substance is split
substance

Q2   catalyst, increases, proteins, amino acids, structural, hormones
Q3 a)   33 °C (accept 32 °C – 34 °C)
b)   They are denatured.
Q4 a)

[Graph: Time taken for reaction / s (y-axis, 20–120) against pH (x-axis, 2–12). Curve starts at 100 at pH 2, drops to a minimum of about 20 at pH 6, then rises to about 105 at pH 12.]

b)   About pH 6.
c)   At very high and very low pH levels the bonds in the enzymes are broken / the enzyme is denatured, meaning that it can't speed up the reaction.
d)   No. This enzyme works very slowly at pH 2.
e)   Any two from: the temperature should be the same at each pH / the same volume of the reactant and enzyme should be used for each pH / the same method of determining when the reaction is complete should be used for each pH / he should measure and time everything as accurately as possible using appropriate equipment.

Page 20 — Enzymes and Digestion

Q1 a)   protease
↓
protein → **amino acids**
b)   lipase
↓
fat → glycerol + fatty acids
c)   amylase
↓
carbohydrate → **sugars**
e.g. starch

Q2

Amylase	Protease	Lipase	Bile
salivary glands	stomach	pancreas	liver
pancreas	pancreas	small intestine	
small intestine	small intestine		

Q3 a)   gall bladder, small intestine, neutralises, enzymes, fat.
b)   Emulsification breaks fat into smaller droplets which gives a larger surface area for lipase to work on, speeding up digestion.

Page 21 — More on Enzymes and Digestion

Q1

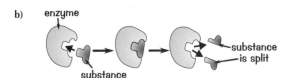

mouth — oesophagus
liver — stomach
gall bladder — pancreas
large intestine — small intestine
rectum

Biology 2b — Enzymes and Genetics

Q2 a) false
b) true
c) true
d) false
Q3 a) Produce saliva / amylase
b) Produces enzymes (protease, amylase and lipase) / releases enzymes into the small intestine.
c) Produces bile which emulsifies fats and neutralises stomach acid.

Page 22 — Enzymes and Respiration

Q1 a) glucose + oxygen → carbon dioxide + water (+ energy)
b) It means respiration that requires oxygen.
Q2 a) i) true
ii) false
iii) true
iv) false
v) true
vi) false
vii) true
viii) true
b) ii) Respiration usually releases energy from glucose.
iv) Respiration takes place in a cell's mitochondria.
vi) Breathing and respiration are completely separate processes.
Q3 E.g. building larger molecules from smaller ones, to allow muscles to contract (in animals), to maintain a certain body temperature (in mammals and birds) and to build sugars, nitrates and other nutrients into amino acids, which are then built up into proteins (in plants).

Pages 23-24 — Exercise

Q1 a) energy, contracting
b) glucose, oxygen
c) rapidly, glycogen
d) anaerobic
e) incomplete
Q2 a) Any two from: e.g. his breathing rate increases / he breathes more deeply / his heart rate increases.
b) i) muscle fatigue
ii) lactic acid
iii) anaerobic respiration
c) While John was respiring anaerobically he created an oxygen debt. When he stops exercising this must be repaid. To do this he breathes deeply to get the necessary oxygen into the muscles to oxidise the lactic acid.
Q3 a) Anaerobic: glucose → lactic acid (+ energy)
b) less
Q4 a) 45 − 15 = **30** breaths per minute
b) The breathing rate increases to provide more oxygen for increased respiration in the muscles, and to remove the extra carbon dioxide produced.
c) 3.5 minutes
Q5 a) Any two from, e.g: measuring their pulse rates by averaging over the same time period. / They should run the same distance. / They should run at the same speed.
b) Saeed

Pages 25-26 — Uses of Enzymes

Q1 a) Enzymes can be used to pre-digest baby food so that it is easier for babies to digest.
b) Enzymes can be used to convert glucose syrup into fructose syrup. Fructose is sweeter than glucose and so less has to be added to sweeten foods (which is good for slimmers).
Q2 a) Lipaclean would be best because it contains lipase enzymes and they digest fat.
b) Because they are allergic to them.
Q3 a) carbohydrates
b) isn't, is
c) carbohydrases
Q4 a) E.g. to speed up reactions.
b) Any two from: temperature, pH and lack of contamination.

c) i) Any two from: e.g you can use lower temperatures and pressures, which means a lower cost as it saves energy / enzymes are specific, so they only catalyse the reaction you want them to / they work for a long time so you can continually use them / they are biodegradable (so they cause less pollution).
ii) E.g. they can be denatured by a small change in temperature / they can be denatured by small changes in pH / they are susceptible to poisons / they can cause allergies / they can be expensive to produce.
Q5 a) E.g. use the same amount of each washing powder / use the same type of food stains / use clothes made of the same type of fabric.
b) i) Powder A
ii) Powder A. Biological detergents contain enzymes, so at low temperatures they work more effectively than other detergents.

Pages 27-28 — DNA

Q1 a) deoxyribonucleic acid
b) cells, chromosomes, section, protein, amino acids
c) 20
d) double helix
e) No, identical twins have the same DNA.
Q2 1. Collect the sample for DNA testing.
2. Cut the DNA into small sections.
3. Separate the sections of DNA.
4. Compare the unique patterns of DNA.
Q3 a) E.g. DNA from a crime scene could be checked against everyone in the country.
b) E.g. it might be an invasion of privacy. / False positives could occur if there was a mistake in the analysis.
Q4

	Foal	Mother	Father
DNA sample	Sample 1	Sample 2	**Sample 4**

Q5 a) The victim and suspect A — they share a significant amount of their DNA.
b) Suspect B
c) Suspect B's DNA matches the DNA found at the crime scene.
d) No. If suspect B's blood was found on the victim's shirt, it doesn't mean that he/she committed the murder. Their blood could have got onto the shirt on a different occasion.

Page 29 — Cell Division — Mitosis

Q1 a) true
b) false (there are 23 pairs of chromosomes)
c) false (they're found in the nucleus)
d) true
e) true
f) true
g) true
Q2 a) Cells that are not dividing contain long strings of DNA.
b) Before a cell divides, it copies (duplicates) its DNA and forms X-shaped chromosomes.
c) The chromosomes line up across the centre of the cell, and then the arms of each chromosome are pulled to opposite ends of the cell.
d) A membrane forms in each half of the cell to form the nuclei.
e) The cytoplasm divides, making two new genetically identical cells.
Q3 reproduce, strawberry, runners, asexual, genes, variation.

Pages 30-31 — Cell Division — Meiosis

Q1 a) true
b) true
c) true
d) true
e) false

Biology 2b — Enzymes and Genetics

Q2 a) Before the cell starts to divide it duplicates its DNA to produce an exact copy.

b) For the first meiotic division the chromosomes line up in their pairs across the centre of the cell.

c) The pairs are pulled apart. Each new cell has only one copy of each chromosome, some from the mother and some from the father.

d) The chromosomes line up across the centre of the nucleus ready for the second division, and the left and right arms are pulled apart.

e) There are now 4 gametes, each containing half the original number of chromosomes.

Q3 a) two

b) 46, 23

c) different

d) half as many

Q4 a)

b)

Q5 a) Sex cells that only have one copy of each chromosome.

b) Gametes have half the usual number of chromosomes so that when two gametes join together during fertilisation the resulting fertilised egg will have the full number of chromosomes.

c) When two gametes fuse, the new individual will have a mixture of two sets of chromosomes — some from its mother and some from its father.

d) mitosis

Page 32 — Stem Cells

Q1 specialised, animal, plant, stem cells

Q2 Embryonic stem cells can differentiate into any type of body cell. Adult stem cells are less versatile — they can only turn into certain types of cell.

Q3 E.g. people with some blood diseases (e.g. sickle cell anaemia) can be treated by bone marrow transplants. Bone marrow contains stem cells that can turn into new blood cells to replace the faulty old ones.

Q4 diabetes — insulin-producing cells
paralysis — nerve cells
heart disease — heart muscle cells

Q5 a) E.g. stem cell research may lead to cures for a wide variety of diseases.

b) E.g. embryos shouldn't be used for experiments as each one is a potential human life.

Page 33 — X and Y Chromosomes

Q1 a) true

b) false

c) true

d) false

Q2 a)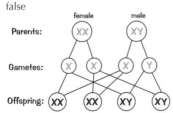

b) The probability is 50% (0.5, 1 in 2, ½).

Q3 a) ZW

b)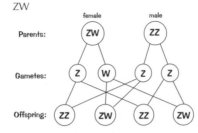

Page 34 — The Work of Mendel

Q1 monk, characteristics, generation, 1866, genetics.

Q2 a) E.g. hereditary units determine the characteristics of an organism. They're passed from parents to offspring. The modern word for them is genes.

b) The dominant hereditary unit is expressed.

Q3 a)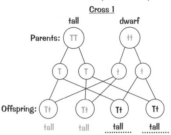

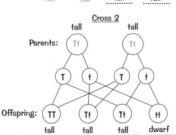

b) 75% (0.75, 3 in 4, ¾)

Pages 35-36 — Genetic Diagrams

Q1 dominant — shown in organisms heterozygous for that trait
genotype — the alleles that an individual contains
heterozygous — having two different alleles for a gene
homozygous — having two identical alleles for a gene
phenotype — the actual characteristics of an individual
recessive — not shown in organisms heterozygous for that trait

Q2 a) Wilma will have brown hair.

b) Wilma has two different alleles for this gene so she is heterozygous for the characteristic.

Q3 a) i) red eyes

ii) white eyes

iii) red eyes

iv) white eyes

b) i)

		parent's alleles	
		R	**r**
parent's alleles	**R**	RR	Rr
	r	Rr	rr

ii) 1/4 or 25%

iii) 12

Biology 2b — Enzymes and Genetics

Q4 a)

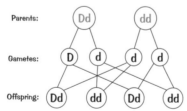

Parents' alleles: SS ss

Gametes' alleles: S S s s

Possible combinations of alleles in offspring: Ss Ss Ss Ss

b) 0% chance of being wrinkled

c)

		parent's alleles	
		S	**s**
parent's alleles	**S**	SS	Ss
	s	Ss	ss

d) True

Pages 37-38 — Genetic Disorders

Q1 a)

Parents: Ff Ff

Gametes: F f F f

Offspring: FF Ff Ff ff

b) i) 25% (quarter, 0.25, 1 in 4, ¼)
ii) 50% (half, 0.5, 1 in 2, ½)
c) 600 000 ÷ 2500 = 240

Q2 a) i)

		Helen's alleles	
		F	**F**
John's alleles	**F**	F F	F F
	f	F f	F f

ii) 0

b) No — cystic fibrosis is a recessive disease, so to suffer from it you must inherit a copy of the faulty allele from both parents. (Mark's wife doesn't have the faulty allele.)

Q3 a) i)

Parents: Dd dd

Gametes: D d d d

Offspring: Dd dd Dd dd

ii) 50% (or 0.5 or ½)
b) A sufferer. Since polydactyly is a dominant disorder, you only need one copy of the defective allele to have it.
c) 100% (or 1)

Q4 a) Possible answers include:
• Embryonic screening implies that genetic disorders are 'undesirable' and may increase prejudice against people with these diseases.
• The rejected embryos are destroyed. Each one could be a human life.
• There's a risk that embryonic screening could be taken too far, e.g. parents might want to choose embryos who fulfil their vision of the ideal child.

b) Possible answers include:
• If embryonic screening means healthy children are born, then this stops the suffering associated with many genetic disorders.
• During IVF, most of the embryos are destroyed anyway — screening just allows the selected one to be healthy.

Pages 39-40 — More Genetic Diagrams

Q1 a)

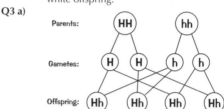

Parents: Gg gg

Gametes: G g g g

Offspring: Gg gg Gg gg

b) 1 : 1 (half grey, half white)
c) 6 grey mice, 6 white mice.
Q2 Sally can cross the plants. If the parent plant with red flowers is thoroughbred (RR) then all their offspring will be red. If the parent plant with red flowers is hybrid (Rr) then there will be an approximate 1 : 1 ratio of red to white offspring.

Q3 a)

Parents: HH hh

Gametes: H H h h

Offspring: Hh Hh Hh Hh

b) i) 1 / 100%
ii) 0
Q4 a) Because plenty of the family carry the allele but aren't sufferers.

b)

	Carrier	Sufferer
Libby	50%	25%
Anne	50%	0%

Q5 a) Dd. Polydactyly is a dominant disorder, so if Amy was DD she would have passed it on to all her children but Brook and Beth are unaffected.
b) i) Dd (Because Alan must be dd because he is not a sufferer. So to be polydactyl, Brian must have inherited Amy's D allele.)
ii)

		Carol	
		D	d
Brian	D	D D	D d
	d	D d	d d

iii) 25% (or 0.25 or ¼)

Pages 41-42 — Fossils

Q1 a) A fossil is the remains of an organism from many years ago.
b) Fossils are usually found in rocks.
Q2 bones, slowly, rock, shaped, clay, hardens, cast
Q3 a) i) A clear yellow 'stone' made from fossilised resin.
ii) There's no oxygen or moisture in amber, so decay microbes can't survive to decay dead organisms. Thus, dead organisms are preserved.
b) No oxygen or moisture — Tar pits
Too acidic — Peat bogs
Too cold — Glaciers
Q4 E.g. many early life forms were soft bodied, so they decayed away completely without leaving fossils.
Fossils that formed a very long time ago may have been destroyed by geological activity (like movement of tectonic plates).
Q5 a) The shell will eventually be replaced with minerals as the sediments around it turn to rock.
b) Fossil B is in a lower layer of rock. It's likely this layer formed first. Subsequent layers built up on top.

Chemistry 2a — Bonding and Calculations

Q6 a) A hypothesis.

b) It was so long ago that it's now very difficult to find any conclusive evidence for the hypothesis or against it.

c) E.g. another theory suggests that life began in a primordial swamp. Simple organic molecules joined to make more complex ones which eventually joined to give life forms.

Pages 43-44 — Extinction and Speciation

Q1 a) Extinct species are those that once lived but that don't exist any more.

b) We mainly know about extinct animals because we have found fossils of them. Also accept: We know more about some animals like mammoths because early people drew pictures of them, or about dodos because people wrote descriptions of them.

Q2 A catastrophic event kills every member of the species — A rare plant that lives on the side of a volcano is wiped out when the volcano erupts.
The environment changes too quickly — An island's rainforest is completely chopped down, destroying the habitat of the striped monkey.
A new disease kills every member of the species — Every member of a species of toad is killed when a new fungal pathogen is accidentally introduced to their habitat.

Q3 a) The development of a new species.

b) Because populations of the same species have become so different that they can't interbreed to give fertile offspring.

c) true

Q4 1 — There are two populations of the same species.
2 — Physical barriers separate the populations.
3 — The populations adapt to their new environments.
4 — A new species develops.

Q5 a) The spiders may have out-competed the squirrels for food (bananas).

b) The gibbons may have been a new predator and hunted the squirrels.

Q6 a) Isolation is where populations of a species are separated.

b) 1. A physical barrier geographically isolates some individuals from the main population.
2. Conditions on either side of a physical barrier are slightly different.
3. Each population shows variation because they have a wide range of alleles.
4. In each population, individuals with characteristics that make them better adapted to their environment have a better chance of survival and so are more likely to breed successfully.
5. The alleles that control the beneficial characteristics are more likely to be passed on to the next generation.
6. Eventually, individuals from the different populations have changed so much that they become separate species.

Pages 45-48 — Mixed Questions — Biology 2b

Q1 a) Stem cells have the ability to differentiate into different types of cell.

b) i) mitosis

ii) Stem cells from embryos can differentiate into all the different types of cells in the human body.

c) Possible answer: Some people feel that using embryos for stem cell research is unethical; they feel that every embryo has a right to life.

Q2 a) White flowers

b) i) FF

ii) ff

iii) Ff

c) 3 purple:1 white, because he is crossing two purple flowers which both have the alleles Ff.

Q3 Recessive, because the parents carry the allele but do not show the characteristics of albinism themselves.

Q4 a)

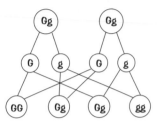

b) i) 3:1

ii) Because fertilisation is random, there is a 1 in 4 chance of each rabbit being white, but this is just a probability and the reality may be different.

c) All of their offspring will be white, because white rabbits are homozygous for the recessive allele (gg) and so cannot be carrying the allele for grey fur.

Q5 a) Fossil X

b) Most animals have hard parts in their bodies e.g. bones or shells. These parts are fossilised more easily.

c) If two organisms can reproduce and produce fertile offspring then they are of the same species. It is not possible to tell if two fossilised animals would have been able to do this.

Q6 a) E.g. her heart rate increased.

b) i) anaerobic respiration

ii) glucose → lactic acid (+ energy)

iii) She had an oxygen debt. She needed to breathe hard to get enough oxygen to oxidise the lactic acid.

c) i) amylase

ii) The salivary glands, the pancreas and the small intestine.

Q7 a) Really long molecules of DNA.

b) In humans, the males are XY and the females are XX.

Q8 a) The amount of DNA is doubling because the DNA is replicating itself.

b) The two daughter cells separate.

c) i) body cells

ii) asexual reproduction

d) E.g. mitosis involves one division whereas meiosis involves two divisions. / Mitosis produces two new cells whereas meiosis produces four new cells. / Mitosis produces identical cells whereas meiosis produces genetically different cells.

Chemistry 2a — Bonding and Calculations

Page 49 — Atoms, Compounds and Isotopes

Q1

Particle	Mass
Proton	1
Neutron	1
Electron	0

Q2 a)

b) The total number of protons and neutrons in an atom.

c) compound

Q3 Isotopes, element, protons, neutrons.

Q4 W and Y, because these two atoms have the same number of protons but a different mass number.

Pages 50-51 — Ionic Bonding

Q1 a) i) true

ii) true

iii) false

iv) true

v) false

vi) true

Chemistry 2a — Bonding and Calculations

b) iii) E.g. atoms form ionic bonds to give them the same electronic structure as the noble gases.

v) E.g. in ionic bonding, electrons from the outer shell are transferred.

Q2 a) 2
b) 2

Q3 a) strong, positive, negative, all directions, large
b) Any two from: e.g. high boiling point / will dissolve to form solutions that conduct electricity / will conduct electricity when molten

Q4 a) i) should be ticked
b) Sodium chloride has a cuboid shape because the electrostatic forces of attraction hold the oppositely charged ions together in a regular lattice arrangement.

Q5 a)

	Conducts electricity?
When solid	No
When dissolved in water	Yes
When molten	Yes

b) When solid, the ions are held tightly in a giant ionic lattice so they're unable to move and conduct electricity. When dissolved or molten, the ions are free to move and so can conduct electricity.

Page 52 — Ions and Formulas

Q1 a) Group 1
b) 1
c) 1^+
d) NaCl

Q2 non-metals, 1^+ charge, negative, 1^- charge

Q3 BeS, K_2S, BeI_2, KI

Q4 a) KBr
b) $FeCl_2$
c) CaF_2

Page 53 — Electronic Structure of Ions

Q1 a)

b)

c)

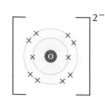

Q2 a) $CaCl_2$
b)

Pages 54-55 — Covalent Bonding

Q1 a) true
b) true
c) true
d) false
e) true

Q2

Atom	Carbon	Chlorine	Hydrogen	Nitrogen	Oxygen
Number of electrons needed to fill outer shell	4	1	1	3	2

Q3 Both atoms need to gain electrons. Sharing electrons allows both atoms to achieve the stable 'full outer shell' of electrons.

Q4 a)

b)

c)

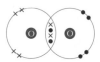

Q5 a)

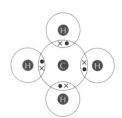

b)

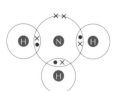

Q6 a) Atoms only share electrons in their outer energy levels/ shells.

b) 1.

2.

Cl — Cl

$\times\times$ $\bullet\bullet$

$\begin{matrix}\times\\\times\end{matrix}$ Cl $\begin{matrix}\times\end{matrix}$ Cl $\begin{matrix}\bullet\\\bullet\end{matrix}$

$\times\times$ $\bullet\bullet$

Pages 56-57 — Covalent Substances: Two Kinds

Q1 Diamond — I am used in drill tips; I am the hardest natural substance; My carbon atoms form four covalent bonds.
Graphite — I have layers which move over one another; I am used in pencils; I am a good conductor of electricity; My carbon atoms form three covalent bonds.
Silicon dioxide — I am also known as silica; I am not made from carbon.

Q2 atoms, strong, high

Q3 a) Any two from: e.g. low melting point / low boiling point / doesn't conduct electricity

Chemistry 2a — Bonding and Calculations

b) E.g. it has weak intermolecular forces so its molecules are easily parted from each other. / There are no ions so there's no electrical charge. / There are no ions to carry the current.

Q4 a) simple molecular and giant covalent/macromolecules
 b) i) silicon dioxide
  ii) graphite
  iii) diamond
 c) Any two from: e.g. it has a very high melting point. / It has a very high boiling point. / It doesn't conduct electricity.

Q5 a) i) Each carbon atom in graphite has one delocalised (free) electron. These free electrons conduct electricity.
  ii) Graphite is made up of layers which are free to slide over each other. There are only weak intermolecular forces between the layers, so graphite is soft and slippery.
 b) Each carbon atom forms four covalent bonds in a very rigid giant covalent structure.

Pages 58-59 — Metallic Structures

Q1 a) giant
 b) heat
 c) atoms

Q2 a) electrons, outer, strong, positive, regular
 b) They have delocalised electrons which are free to move through the whole structure and conduct electricity.

Q3 a) An alloy is a mixture of two or more metals.
 b) In pure metals the regular layers of atoms are able to slide over each other. This means they can be bent. However, in alloys there are atoms of more than one size. This distorts the layers and prevents them from being able to slide over each another. This makes brass harder than copper.

Q4 a) giant ionic
 b) giant covalent
 c) giant metallic

Q5

Property	Giant Ionic	Giant Covalent	Simple Molecular	Giant Metallic
High melting and boiling points	✓	✓	✗	✓
Can conduct electricity when solid	✗	✗ except graphite	✗	✓
Can conduct electricity when molten	✓	✗ except graphite	✗	✓

Q6 a) giant ionic — it only conducts electricity when molten or dissolved.
 b) giant covalent — high melting point, but doesn't conduct electricity.
 c) simple molecular — low melting point.
 d) giant metallic — conducts electricity.

Pages 60-61 — New Materials

Q1 a) i) true
  ii) false
  iii) true
 b) E.g. nitinol is affected by temperature.
 c) It remembers its original shape — so if you bend it out of shape, you can heat it and it goes back to its 'remembered' shape.
 d) E.g. dental braces / glasses frames

Q2 a) hundred, different
 b) They have a huge surface area to volume ratio.

Q3 $1 ÷ 0.000\ 001 =$ **1 000 000 nm**

Q4 a) fullerenes, molecules, hexagonal, atoms
 b) Lightweight but strong — Building materials
 Can detect specific molecules — Sensors to test water purity
 Act like ball bearings to reduce friction — Lubricants for artificial joints
 c) nanoscience
 d) They are so small that they are absorbed more easily by the body than most particles.

Q5 a) They can conduct electricity.
 b) The carbon atoms in nanotubes are joined by covalent bonds which makes them very strong.

Page 62 — Polymers

Q1 a) A
 b) Thermosetting polymers have strong intermolecular forces called crosslinks between the polymer chains.

Q2 What the starting materials are and what the reaction conditions are.

Q3 a) LDP — toothpaste tubes need to be flexible so you can squeeze the paste out.
 b) LDP — freezer bags also need to be flexible.
 c) HDP — The equipment needs to have a high softening temperature so it can be sterilised by heating.

Page 63 — Relative Formula Mass

Q1 a) How heavy an atom of an element is compared to an atom of carbon-12.
 b) i) 24
  ii) 20
  iii) 16
  iv) 1
  v) 12
  vi) 63.5
  vii) 39
  viii) 40
  ix) 35.5

Q2 Element A is helium
 Element B is $(3 × 4) = 12 =$ carbon
 Element C is $(4 × 4) = 16 =$ oxygen

Q3 a) You add the A_r of all the atoms in the compound together.
 b) i) $(2 × 1) + 16 = 18$
  ii) $39 + 16 + 1 = 56$
  iii) $1 + 14 + (3 × 16) = 63$
  iv) $(2 × 1) + 32 + (4 × 16) = 98$
  v) $14 + (4 × 1) + 14 + (3 × 16) = 80$

Q4 $2XOH + H_2 = 114$
 $2 × (X + 16 + 1) + (2 × 1) = 114$
 $2 × (X + 17) + 2 = 114$
 $2 × (X + 17) = 112$
 $X + 17 = 56$
 $X = 39$
 so $X =$ potassium

Page 64 — Two Formula Mass Calculations

Q1 a) Percentage mass of an element in a compound =
 $$\frac{A_r × \text{No. of atoms (of that element)}}{M_r \text{ (of whole compound)}} × 100$$
 b) i) $(14 × 2) ÷ [14 + (4 × 1) + 14 + (3 × 16)] × 100 = 35\%$
  ii) $(4 × 1) ÷ [14 + (4 × 1) + 14 + (3 × 16)] × 100 = 5\%$
  iii) $(3 × 16) ÷ [14 + (4 × 1) + 14 + (3 × 16)] × 100 = 60\%$

Q2 a) $A = (3 × 16) ÷ [(2 × 56) + (3 × 16)] × 100 = 30\%$
 $B = 16 ÷ [(2 × 1) + 16] × 100 = 89\%$
 $C = (3 × 16) ÷ [40 + 12 + (3 × 16)] × 100 = 48\%$
 b) B

Q3 a) $14 ÷ (14 + 16) × 100 = 47\%$
 b)

	Nitrogen	Oxygen
Percentage mass (%)	30.4	69.6
$÷ A_r$	$(30.4 ÷ 14) = 2.17$	$(69.6 ÷ 16) = 4.35$
Ratio	1	2

empirical formula = NO_2

Chemistry 2a — Bonding and Calculations

Q4

	Calcium	Oxygen	Hydrogen
Mass (g)	0.8	0.64	0.04
÷ A_r	(0.8 ÷ 40) = 0.02	(0.64 ÷ 16) = 0.04	(0.04 ÷ 1) = 0.04
Ratio	1	2	2

empirical formula = $Ca(OH)_2$ (or CaO_2H_2)

Pages 65-66 — Calculating Masses in Reactions

Q1 a) $2Mg + O_2 \rightarrow 2MgO$
b)
2Mg
$2 \times 24 = 48$
$48 ÷ 48 = 1$ g
$1 \times 10 = 10$ g

2MgO
$2 \times (24 + 16) = 80$
$80 ÷ 48 = 1.67$ g
$1.67 \times 10 =$ **16.7 g**

Q2
4Na
$4 \times 23 = 92$
$92 ÷ 124 = 0.74$ g
$0.74 \times 2 =$ **1.5 g**

$2Na_2O$
$2 \times [(2 \times 23) + 16] = 124$
$124 ÷ 124 = 1$ g
$1 \times 2 = 2$ g

Q3 a) $2Al + Fe_2O_3 \rightarrow Al_2O_3 + 2Fe$
b)
Fe_2O_3
$[(2 \times 56) + (3 \times 16)] = 160$
$160 ÷ 160 = 1$ g
$1 \times 20 = 20$ g

2Fe
$2 \times 56 = 112$
$112 ÷ 160 = 0.7$
$0.7 \times 20 =$ **14 g**

Q4 $CaCO_3 \rightarrow CaO + CO_2$
$CaCO_3$
$40 + 12 + (3 \times 16) = 100$
$100 ÷ 56 = 1.786$ kg
$1.786 \times 100 =$ **178.6 kg**

CaO
$40 + 16 = 56$
$56 ÷ 56 = 1$ kg
$1 \times 100 = 100$ kg

Q5 a)
C
12
$12 ÷ 12 = 1$ g
$1 \times 10 = 10$ g

2CO
$2 \times (12 + 16) = 56$
$56 ÷ 12 = 4.67$ g
$4.67 \times 10 = 46.7$ g

46.7 g of CO is produced in stage B — all this is used in stage C.
3CO
$3 \times (12 + 16) = 84$
$84 ÷ 84 = 1$ g
$1 \times 46.7 = 46.7$ g

$3CO_2$
$3 \times [12 + (2 \times 16)] = 132$
$132 ÷ 84 = 1.57$ g
$1.57 \times 46.7 =$ **73.3 g**

b) It could be recycled and used in stage B.
Q6 a) $2NaOH + H_2SO_4 \rightarrow Na_2SO_4 + 2H_2O$
b)
2NaOH
$2 \times (23 + 16 + 1) = 80$
$80 ÷ 142 = 0.56$ g
$0.56 \times 75 =$ **42 g**

Na_2SO_4
$(2 \times 23) + 32 + (4 \times 16) = 142$
$142 ÷ 142 = 1$ g
$1 \times 75 = 75$ g

c)
H_2SO_4
$(2 \times 1) + 32 + (4 \times 16) = 98$
$98 ÷ 98 = 1$ g
$1 \times 50 = 50$ g

$2H_2O$
$2 \times [(2 \times 1) + 16] = 36$
$36 ÷ 98 = 0.37$ g
$0.37 \times 50 =$ **18.5 g**

Page 67 — Percentage Yield and Reversible Reactions

Q1 a) yield, higher, percentage yield, predicted
b) $(6 ÷ 15) \times 100 = 40\%$
c) When the solution was filtered a bit of barium sulfate may have been lost. Less product means a lower percentage yield.
d) i) Not all the reactants are turned into products because the reaction goes both ways. So the percentage yield is reduced.
ii) The unexpected reaction will use up the reactants, so there's not as much left to make the product you want. So the percentage yield is reduced.
Q2 E.g. a low yield means wasted chemicals which isn't sustainable. Increasing the yield would save resources for the future.

Page 68 — Chemical Analysis and Instrumental Methods

Q1 a) Extract the colour from the sweet by placing it in a small cup with a few drops of solvent. Put a spot of the coloured solution on a pencil baseline on filter paper. Put the paper in a beaker of solvent (keep the baseline above the solvent). After the solvent has seeped up the paper, measure the distance the dyes have travelled. Repeat for each sweet.
b) Blue has 2 dyes.
c) Brown, because the same pattern of dyes are present.
Q2 a) E.g. they're very fast
b) E.g. they're very accurate and very sensitive/can detect even the tiniest amounts of a substance.
Q3 a) i) 2
ii) 6 and 10 minutes
b) Work out the relative molecular mass of each of the substances from the graph it draws.

Pages 69-71 — Mixed Questions — Chemistry 2a

Q1 a) i) giant covalent
ii) All the atoms are bonded to each other by strong covalent bonds so it takes a lot of energy to separate the carbon atoms.
b) i) T
ii) nanoparticle / fullerene
Q2 a)

	Silicon	Chlorine
Mass (g)	1.4	7.1
÷ A_r	(1.4 ÷ 28) = 0.05	(7.1 ÷ 35.5) = 0.2
Ratio	1	4

Empirical formula = $SiCl_4$
b) $(35.5 \times 4) ÷ [(35.5 \times 4) + 28] \times 100 =$ **83.5%**
c) $Si + 2Cl_2 \rightarrow SiCl_4$
d)
Si
28
$28 ÷ 28 = 1$ g
$1 \times 1.4 = 1.4$ g

$SiCl_4$
$28 + (4 \times 35.5) = 170$
$170 ÷ 28 = 6.07$ g
$6.07 \times 1.4 =$ **8.5 g**

Q3 a) Any one from: A / B / F.
Simple molecular substances have weak intermolecular forces and therefore low melting and boiling points. / They do not conduct electricity since there are no ions and so no charge.
b) C
c) All metals are good conductors of electricity when solid. / Substance D is a poor conductor of electricity when solid.
Q4 a) false
b) false
c) true
Q5 a) $24 + [2 \times (14 + 16 \times 3)] = 148$
b)
Mg
24
$24 ÷ 24 = 1$ g
$1 \times 12 = 12$ g

$Mg(NO_3)_2$
$24 + [2 \times (14 + 16 \times 3)] = 148$
$148 ÷ 24 = 6.17$ g
$6.17 \times 12 =$ **74 g**

c) E.g. in a reversible reaction some of the products turn back into the reactants. / Unexpected reactions can take place and use up some of the reactants. / Some liquid or solid can be lost during filtration.
Q6 a) i) ionic compound
ii) metal
iii) alloy
b) i) substance i) (ionic compound)
ii) Ionic substances don't conduct electricity when solid as the ions are not free to move.
c) $CaCl_2$
Q7 a) gas, speeds, chromatograph, compounds, retention time, identify, mass spectrometer
b) E.g. it's more accurate.

Chemistry 2b — Reaction Rates, Salts and Electrolysis

Chemistry 2b — Reaction Rates, Salts and Electrolysis

Page 72 — Rate of Reaction

Q1 a) higher
b) lower
c) decreases
d) does
Q2 a) i) Z
ii) It has the steepest gradient. / It becomes flat sooner.
b) Equal masses of marble chips were used each time.
c) The curve should be steeper and show that a larger volume of gas is produced, e.g. like this:

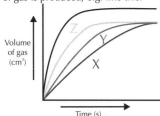

Q3 a) decrease
b) More reactant was used.
c) The reactants in Q might be in smaller pieces/have a larger surface area/be more concentrated/be at a higher temperature.

Pages 73-74 — Measuring Rates of Reaction

Q1 rate, reactants, formed, precipitation, faster, gas, mass, volume
Q2 a) C
b) i) Point K: 0.08 ÷ 5 = 0.016 g/s
ii) Point L: 0.06 ÷ 15 = 0.004 g/s
Q3 a)

Average volume of gas produced (cm³)
94
64
45.5
35
9

b) 50 in the third column of the table should be circled.
c) 2 mol/dm³
d) i) gas syringe
ii) Any one from: e.g. stopwatch / stopclock / timer / balance / measuring cylinder
e) Sketch should look something like this:

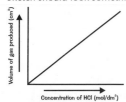

f) To improve the reliability of his results.
g) E.g. misreading the value from the gas syringe. / Not emptying the gas syringe before starting.

Pages 75-78 — Rate of Reaction Experiments

Q1 increase, faster, smaller, react
Q2 a) B

b) Curve should look something like this:

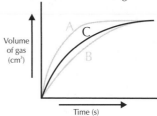

c) Size of marble pieces.
d) No, you cannot tell if it was a fair test. The same mass of marble chips was used each time but it is not known if the same volume of HCl was used each time or if the temperature was kept constant.
e) Measuring how quickly the reaction loses mass.
Q3 a) 13 (he took one at the start).
b) x-axis: time (s)
y-axis: change/loss in mass (g)
c)

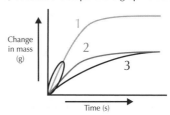

d) 145.73 – 143.89 = 1.84 g
Q4 a) 1, because the slope of the graph is steepest.
b)

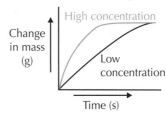

c) The reactions finish eventually. / The reactants are always used up eventually.
Q5 The mixture goes cloudy.
Q6 a) water bath, stopclock, thermometer.
b) i) faster
ii) 145 s
c) i) temperature
ii) time taken for cross to disappear
d) Repeat the investigation to get more results and find the average for each temperature.
Q7 Increasing the concentration of HCl increases the rate of reaction.
Q8 a) $2H_2O$
b) C
c) increase
Q9 a) Volume of gas (cm³/dm³/l/ml)
b) i) R
ii) Reaction R has the steepest graph and becomes flat sooner, so it is the fastest reaction and must have the most effective catalyst.

Page 79 — Collision Theory

Q1 increasing the temperature — makes the particles move faster, so they collide more often
decreasing the concentration — means fewer particles of reactant are present, so less frequent collisions occur
increasing the surface area — gives particles a bigger area of solid reactant to react with
Q2 a) energy
b) faster, more
c) rate of reaction

Chemistry 2b — Reaction Rates, Salts and Electrolysis

Q3 a) i) increase
   ii) The particles are closer together so collisions happen more frequently.

b)

low pressure   high pressure

Q4 a) false
   b) true
   c) false
   d) true

Page 80 — Collision Theory and Catalysts

Q1 Activation energy is the minimum amount of energy needed by particles to react.

Q2 a) A catalyst is a substance which speeds up a reaction, without being changed or used up in the reaction.
   b) i) A
      ii) Reaction A has the steepest graph and becomes flat sooner so it's the fastest reaction. This means it must have used a catalyst.

Q3 a) Any one from: e.g. they allow the reaction to take place at a much lower temperature. This reduces the energy used which saves money. / They increase the rate of the reaction, so costs are reduced because the plant doesn't have to operate for as long.
   b) Any two from: e.g. they can be expensive to buy. / A plant making more than one product will need more than one catalyst. / They can be poisoned by impurities and stop working.
   c) E.g. the Haber process uses an iron catalyst.

Pages 81-82 — Energy Transfer in Reactions

Q1 to, heat, rise, temperature
Q2 a) N, B
   b) combustion
   c) E.g. adding sodium to water.
Q3 take in, heat, fall/decrease
Q4 a) thermal decomposition
   b) i) endothermic
      ii) The reaction takes in heat from the surroundings.
   c) i) $1\,800\,000 \div 1000 = 1800$ kJ
      ii) $90\,000 \div 1\,800\,000 = 0.05$ tonnes or 50 kg
Q5 a) When he dropped water on it. / When it turned blue. / The second part.
   b) When he heated up the copper sulphate. / The first part. / When it went white.
   c) hydrated.
   d) hydrated copper sulfate $\rightleftharpoons$ anhydrous copper sulfate + water
   e) reversible reaction
Q6 a) X
   b) N
   c) X
   d) N

Pages 83-84 — Acids and Alkalis

Q1 a) acid + base $\rightarrow$ **salt** + **water**
   b) neutralisation
   c) i) $H^+_{(aq)}$ and $OH^-_{(aq)}$
      ii) $H^+_{(aq)}$
      iii) $OH^-_{(aq)}$
      iv) $OH^-_{(aq)}$
      v) $H^+_{(aq)}$
Q2 a) neutral

b) E.g. universal indicator
c) 7
d) alkali
Q3 a) $HCl_{(aq)} + NaOH_{(aq)} \rightarrow$ **$NaCl_{(aq)}$** + $H_2O_{(l)}$
   b) $H^+_{(aq)} + OH^-_{(aq)} \rightarrow H_2O_{(l)}$
   c) an indicator (e.g. Universal indicator)
   d) pH 7
Q4 a) s
   b) l
   c) g
   d) aq
Q5 a) baking soda or soap powder
   b) They are weak bases and so would neutralise the acid but wouldn't irritate or harm the skin. (Stronger bases like caustic soda might damage the skin.)

Q6 a)

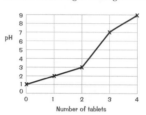

b) The pH increases from pH 1 to pH 9. (It increases most sharply between pH 3 and pH 7.)
c) 3

Pages 85-86 — Acids Reacting with Metals

Q1 a)

sulfuric acid
hydrogen
aluminium

   b) aluminium + **sulfuric acid** $\rightarrow$ aluminium sulfate + **hydrogen**
   c) $2Al + 3H_2SO_4 \rightarrow Al_2(SO_4)_3 + 3H_2$
   d) zinc + sulfuric acid $\rightarrow$ zinc sulfate + hydrogen
   e) $Mg + 2HCl \rightarrow MgCl_2 + H_2$
Q2 a) A
   b) B
   c) A: magnesium
      B: copper
      C: iron
      D: zinc
Q3 a) E.g. the number of gas bubbles produced in a certain time. / The time it takes for the metal to disappear completely. / The volume of gas produced in a certain time. / Loss of mass in a certain time.
   b) acid concentration
   c) Any two from: e.g. volume of acid. / Mass of the metal pieces. / Size of the metal pieces. / Temperature.
Q4 metals, hydrogen, copper, reactive, more, chloride, sulfuric, nitric
Q5 a) i) $Ca + 2HCl \rightarrow CaCl_2 + H_2$
      ii) $2Na + 2HCl \rightarrow 2NaCl + H_2$
      iii) $2Li + H_2SO_4 \rightarrow Li_2SO_4 + H_2$
   b) i) magnesium bromide
      ii) $2Al + 6HBr \rightarrow 2AlBr_3 + 3H_2$

Pages 87-88 — Oxides, Hydroxides and Ammonia

Q1 a) hydrochloric acid + lead oxide $\rightarrow$ **lead** chloride + water
   b) nitric acid + copper hydroxide $\rightarrow$ copper **nitrate** + water
   c) sulfuric acid + zinc oxide $\rightarrow$ zinc sulfate + **water**
   d) hydrochloric acid + **nickel** oxide $\rightarrow$ nickel **chloride** + **water**
   e) **nitric** acid + copper oxide $\rightarrow$ **copper** nitrate + **water**
   f) sulfuric acid + **sodium** hydroxide $\rightarrow$ sodium **sulfate** + **water**

Chemistry 2b — Reaction Rates, Salts and Electrolysis

Q2 a) The following should be ticked:
Acids react with metal oxides to form a salt and water.
Salts and water are formed when acids react with metal hydroxides.
Ammonia solution is alkaline.

b) $H_2SO_4 + CuO \rightarrow CuSO_4 + H_2O$
$HCl + NaOH \rightarrow NaCl + H_2O$

Q3 a) E.g. potassium oxide/hydroxide + sulfuric acid

b) ammonia + hydrochloric acid

c) E.g. silver oxide/hydroxide + nitric acid

Q4 a) NH_3

b) alkaline, nitrogen, proteins, salts, fertilisers

c) ammonia + nitric acid → ammonium nitrate

d) Because it has nitrogen from two sources, the ammonia and the nitric acid.

e) No water is produced.

Q5 a) i) $CuO_{(s)}$

ii) $H_2O_{(l)}$

iii) $HCl_{(aq)}$

iv) $ZnO_{(s)}$

v) $Na_2SO_{4(aq)} + 2H_2O_{(l)}$

b) i) $2NaOH + H_2SO_4 \rightarrow Na_2SO_4 + 2H_2O$

ii) $Mg(OH)_2 + 2HNO_3 \rightarrow Mg(NO_3)_2 + 2H_2O$

iii) $2NH_3 + H_2SO_4 \rightarrow (NH_4)_2SO_4$

Pages 89-90 — Making Salts

Q1 a) soluble

b) insoluble

c) acids, neutralised

d) precipitation

Q2 a) B

b) C

c) A

Q3 a) **silver nitrate** + **sodium chloride** → silver chloride + **sodium nitrate**

b) The silver chloride must be filtered out of the solution. It needs to be washed and then dried on filter paper.

c) E.g. the removal of poisonous ions from drinking water. / The removal of calcium and magnesium ions from hard water.

Q4 a) The nickel oxide will sink to the bottom of the flask.

b) i)

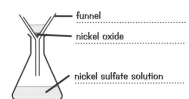

funnel
nickel oxide
nickel sulfate solution

ii) filtration

c) Evaporate some of the water (to make the solution more concentrated) and then leave the rest to evaporate very slowly.

d) nickel and nickel hydroxide

e) i) As potassium hydroxide is a soluble base, you can't tell when the reaction is finished — you can't just add an excess of solid to the acid and filter out what's left.

ii) You have to add exactly the right amount of alkali to just neutralise the acid — you need to use an indicator to show when the reaction's finished. Then repeat using exactly the same volumes of alkali and acid so the salt isn't contaminated with indicator.

Page 91 — Electrolysis

Q1 electric current, ionic, molten, elements, electrolysis, liquid, free ions, conduct, flow, positive, negative, atoms/molecules, molecules/atoms

Q2 a) It could be melted.

b) lead and bromine

c) i) true

ii) false

iii) true

iv) false

v) false

Page 92 — Electrolysis of Sodium Chloride Solution

Q1 a) The product is hydrogen unless the metal ions are less reactive than hydrogen — in which case the metal ions will form atoms.

b) hydrogen

Q2 sodium chloride, chlorine, plastics/bleach, bleach/plastics, negative electrode, sodium hydroxide, soap

Q3 a) A: H^+
B: Cl^-
C: H_2
D: Cl_2

b) Positive electrode: $2Cl^- \rightarrow Cl_2 + 2e^-$
Negative electrode: $2H^+ + 2e^- \rightarrow H_2$

Page 93 — Extraction of Aluminium and Electroplating

Q1 a) i) bauxite

ii) aluminium oxide, Al_2O_3

b) i) false

ii) true

iii) true

iv) false

v) false

c) The oxygen produced at the positive electrode reacts with the carbon in the electrode to produce carbon dioxide. So the positive electrodes gradually get 'eaten away'.

Q2 a)

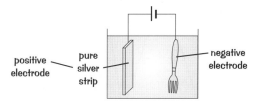

positive electrode
pure silver strip
negative electrode

b) silver/Ag^+

c) E.g. to make it look attractive without the expense of making it from solid silver.

d) E.g. plating metals for electronic circuits / computers.

Pages 94-96 — Mixed Questions — Chemistry 2b

Q1 a) Increasing the temperature.
Increasing the concentration of the reactants (or the pressure if it's a gas).
Adding a catalyst.
Increasing the surface area of solid reactants.

b) The amount of product formed.

Q2 a) Q

b) R

c) Measure the volume of gas given off using a gas syringe.

Q3 a) true

b) true

c) false

d) true

e) true

Q4 a) i) acidic

ii) alkaline

b) i) neutralisation

ii) exothermic

Q5 a) $Mg + 2HCl \rightarrow MgCl_2 + H_2$

b) The pH would increase. / It would become less acidic, until it finally reached neutral/pH 7 (if there was enough magnesium).

Physics 2a — Motion, Energy and Electricity

c) Magnesium sulfate.

Q6 a) i) They gain electrons to become aluminium atoms again.

ii) $Al^{3+}_{(aq)} + 3e^- \rightarrow Al_{(s)}$

b) $2O^{2-}_{(aq)} \rightarrow O_{2(g)} + 4e^-$

Q7 Aluminium oxide has a very high melting point. Dissolving it in molten cryolite brings the melting point down. This reduces the energy needed and makes the electrolysis cheaper.

Q8 a) i) $MgCl_2$

ii) $MgO_{(s)} + 2HCl_{(aq)} \rightarrow MgCl_{2(aq)} + H_2O_{(l)}$

b) sulfuric acid/H_2SO_4

c) bases

Q9 a) i) hydrogen and chlorine

ii) E.g. chlorine is used in the manufacture of plastics. / Chlorine is used in the manufacture of bleach.

b) The sodium ions stay in solution because they're more reactive than hydrogen. Hydroxide ions from water are also left behind. This means that sodium hydroxide (NaOH) is left in the solution.

c) Coating the surface of one metal with another metal.

Physics 2a
— Motion, Energy and Electricity

Page 97 — Velocity and Distance-Time Graphs

Q1 −12 m/s

Q2 a) 180 s (or 3 mins)

b) Speed = gradient of graph = distance ÷ time
Speed = 450 ÷ 180 = **2.5 m/s**

c) He runs there in half the time it took him to walk there — 90 s. So the graph looks like this:

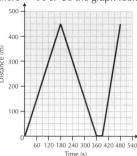

Q3 The graph shows that the motorist accelerates for about 1.5 seconds, then travels at a constant speed. So the gradient of the graph between 1.5 s and 3.0 s will give you the speed.
Gradient = vertical change ÷ horizontal change = (72 − 18) ÷ (3.0 − 1.5) = 54 ÷ 1.5 = **36 m/s** — i.e. she was exceeding the speed limit. So the motorist wasn't telling the truth.

Pages 98-99 — Acceleration and Velocity-Time Graphs

Q1 a) The car accelerates from rest, so the change in velocity is **20 m/s**.
Acceleration = change in velocity ÷ time taken = 20 ÷ 3.5 = **5.7 m/s^2**.

b) Change in velocity = 20 − 3 = 17 m/s.
So acceleration = 17 ÷ 2.8 = **6.1 m/s^2**.
The car has a greater acceleration than before. (This assumes that the modified car's acceleration from 0 to 3 m/s is not slower.)

Q2 a) Since the egg was dropped from rest, its change in speed is 80 m/s. So acceleration = 80 ÷ 8 = **10 m/s^2**.

b) Now rearrange the formula to get time taken
Time taken = change in velocity ÷ acceleration = 40 ÷ 10 = **4 s**

Q3 Rearranging the formula for acceleration you get:
change in speed = acceleration × time = 2 × 4 = 8 m/s.
Change in speed = final speed − initial speed,
so initial speed = final speed − change in speed = 24 − 8 = **16 m/s**.

Q4 Acceleration = gradient = 8 ÷ 5 = **1.6 m/s^2**.

Q5 **A** — (constant) acceleration (from 0 - 3 m/s)
B — constant speed (of 3 m/s)
C — (constant) acceleration (from 3 - 9 m/s)
D — constant speed (of 9 m/s)
E — (constant) deceleration (from 9 - 7 m/s)

Q6 The distance the bus driver travelled before stopping is equal to the area under the graph. To find it, split the graph into a rectangle and a triangle.
Area of the rectangle = base × height = 0.75 × 12 = 9 m.
Area of the triangle = half × base × height = 0.5 × 2.5 × 12 = 15 m. Total distance = 9 m + 15 m = **24 m**.
He didn't hit the piglet.

Page 100 — Weight, Mass and Gravity

Q1 mass, kilograms, weight, newtons, gravitational

Q2 a) W = m × g
m = 58 kg, g = 10 N/kg
W = 58 × 10 = **580 N**

b) Change in weight = 580 − 460 = 120 N
Change in mass = change in weight ÷ g = 120 ÷ 10 = **12 kg**

Q3 a) Mass is the amount of matter, which stays constant. Weight is the force of gravity on this mass, and as the gravity is a different strength on Mars her weight changes.

b) Mass = weight ÷ gravitational field strength, which on Earth is 10 N/kg, so the rock has a mass of 5 kg.
1.9 kg ÷ 5 kg = 0.38
The scales read 38% of the true mass, so the gravitational field strength on Mars is 38% of that on Earth. 10 N/kg × 0.38 = **3.8 N/kg** (or m/s^2).

Page 101 — Resultant Forces

Q1 a) The teapot's weight is balanced by a reaction force from the table.

b) i) No. The teapot is accelerating so the forces can't be balanced.

ii) The reaction force from the floor.

Q2 a)

b) No — he is decelerating. South.

Q3 a) 1 500 000 − 1 500 000 = 0 N

b) 6 000 000 − 1 500 000 = 4 500 000 N

Q4 a) There is a resultant force — the ball is slowing down, which is deceleration.

b) There is a resultant force — motion in a circle means constantly changing direction, which requires acceleration.

c) There is no resultant force — the vase is stationary on the window ledge.

Pages 102-104 — Forces and Acceleration

Q1 balanced, stationary, constant, non-zero, accelerates, resultant force, interact, opposite

Q2 The third statement should be ticked — The driving force of the engine is equal to friction and air resistance combined.

Q3 a) Statement **C** should be circled — The thrust is equal to the air resistance and the lift is equal to the weight.

Physics 2a — Motion, Energy and Electricity

b) i) The thrust is **less than** the air resistance.
ii) The lift is **less than** the weight.
Q4 Force = mass × acceleration.
Disraeli 9000: 800 kg × 5 m/s^2 = 4000 N
Palmerston 6i: 1560 kg × 0.7 m/s^2 = 1092 N
Heath TT: 950 kg × 3 m/s^2 = 2850 N
Asquith 380: 790 kg × 2 m/s^2 = 1580 N
So the correct order is: **Palmerston 6i, Asquith 380, Heath TT, Disraeli 9000.**
Q5 a) The force of the engine is 110 kg × 2.80 m/s^2 = **308 N.**
b) Mass = force ÷ acceleration = 308 ÷ 1.71 **= 180 kg** (to 3 s.f.).
Q6 Using F = ma, the resultant force on the mass must be 1 kg × 0.25 m/s^2 = 0.25 N.
Resultant force = force on the newton-meter – force of friction (they act in opposite directions).
0.25 N = 0.4 N – force of friction, so force of friction = 0.4 N – 0.25 N = **0.15 N.**
Q7 The third statement should be ticked — The car's pulling force accelerates the caravan. The caravan's reaction acts on the car, not the caravan.
Q8 The first statement should be ticked — Your feet push backwards on the ground, so the ground pushes you forwards.
Q9 a) i) The van is travelling at a steady speed, so the resultant force must be 0. So the force exerted by the engine must be equal to the air resistance and friction combined.
2000 N + 500 N = **2500 N.**
ii)

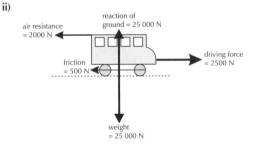

reaction of ground = 25 000 N
air resistance = 2000 N
friction = 500 N
driving force = 2500 N
weight = 25 000 N

b) The resultant force will now be 200 N (forces were previously balanced)
a = F/m = 200 ÷ 2500 = **0.08 m/s^2.**
c) The resultant driving force is now maximum driving force – (force of wind + friction + air resistance) = 2650 – 2700 = –50 N. This force acts in the opposite direction to the van's movement, so the van will continue to decelerate, but at a slower rate (0.02 m/s^2).

Pages 105-106 — Frictional Force and Terminal Velocity

Q1 greater, accelerates, increase, balances, constant, greater, decelerates, decrease, balances, constant.
Q2 All the boxes except 'carrying less cargo' should be ticked.
Q3 a) Paola is **wrong** because although gravity (the accelerating force per unit mass) is the same for both objects, air resistance will affect them differently because they have different shapes.
b) Guiseppe is **right** because drag will be greater for the feather compared to its weight, so drag will balance its weight sooner. The hammer will continue to accelerate for longer than the feather.
Q4 No, Mavis can't draw any conclusions. The terminal velocity depends not only on drag (which is determined by the size, shape and smoothness of the object) but on the weight of the object, and the weights of the balls will be different.
Q5 Region A: weight is greater
Region B: both equal
Region C: air resistance is greater
Region D: both equal

Q6 a) No, Kate isn't really moving upwards. She only **seems** to move upwards when she opens her parachute because she slows down relative to the camera (which is held by Alison — who hasn't opened her parachute yet).
b) She decelerates until she reaches her terminal velocity and then falls at this speed until she lands.
Q7 a) Venus's atmosphere is much thicker than Earth's so a parachute the same size or smaller would provide enough drag to slow the probe to a safe speed.
b) Mars has lower gravity, so less drag is required to balance the probe's weight, but there is much less resistance from the thinner atmosphere, so the parachute would have to be larger than one used on Earth.

Page 107 — Stopping Distances

Q1 a) The distance the car travels under the braking force before it comes to a stop.
b) The distance the car travels during the driver's reaction time.
Q2

Thinking Distance	Braking Distance
tiredness alcohol speed drugs	road surface tyres weather brakes speed load

Q3 The total stopping distance will increase. Both thinking and braking distance will increase.
Q4 The friction between the brake discs and pads will be reduced if they are covered in water. This means the braking force will be reduced and the car will take longer to stop (i.e. the braking distance increases).
Q5 E.g. distractions like mobile phones won't affect Sam's thinking distance, as thinking distance is the distance travelled between the driver first spotting a hazard and taking action. However, it will mean that she will be less likely to notice a hazard until she is much closer to it. (So she is much more likely to crash if there is a hazard.)

Pages 108-109 — Work and Potential Energy

Q1 a) Work done and energy transferred are the same thing, so Jenny does **50 J** of work.
b) Distance = work done ÷ force = 50 ÷ 250 = **0.2 m**
Q2 To push your bicycle you need to apply a force to overcome resistant forces like friction. The work done is equal to the force you apply (in the direction of motion) multiplied by the distance you push your bike.
Q3 a) True
b) False
c) True
d) True
e) False (E_p = m × g × h = 3 × 10 × 2.5 = **75 J**)
Q4 a) E_p = m × g × h = 25 kg × 10 N/kg × 1.2 m = **300 J.**
b) Total E_p = 28 × 300 J = **8400 J.**
c) The energy transferred and the work done by Dave are the same thing, so **8400 J.**
Q5 a) Distance = work done ÷ force = 80 000 ÷ 50 N = **1600 m**
b) i) Work = force × distance, so force = work ÷ distance = 90 000 ÷ 120 = **750 N.**
weight / gravity
ii) Work = gravitational potential energy = mass × g × height, so mass = work ÷ (g × height)
mass = 90 000 ÷ (10 × 120) = **75 kg**
(OR: Weight = mass × g
so mass = weight ÷ g = 750 ÷10 = **75 kg**)
Q6 a) Rearrange E_p = mass × g × height:
height = E_p ÷ (m × g) = 4000 ÷ (50 × 10) = 8 m
b) The energy converted from potential energy to kinetic energy is 1500 J, so the difference must be the wasted energy. 4000 J – 1500 J = **2500 J.**

Physics 2a — Motion, Energy and Electricity

c) friction

d) Force = work ÷ distance = 2500 ÷ 50 = **50 N**

e) Energy wasted = 4000 J – 2000 J = **2000 J**.
Force = 2000 ÷ 50 = **40 N**

f) The mat reduces the amount of friction. Less energy is wasted and so more potential energy is converted into kinetic energy.

g) Force = 2000 ÷ 5 = **400 N**

Page 110 — Kinetic Energy

Q1 a) true

b) false

c) true

Q2 a) Just before the ball hits the ground, it has converted all of its potential energy into kinetic energy, so it has **242 J** of kinetic energy.

b)
$$v = \sqrt{\frac{2 \times E_k}{m}} = \sqrt{\frac{2 \times 242}{0.1}} = 69.6 \text{ m/s}$$

Q3 a) i)
$$v = \sqrt{\frac{2 \times E_k}{m}} = \sqrt{\frac{2 \times 614\,400}{1200}} = 32 \text{ m/s}$$

ii)
$$v = \sqrt{\frac{2 \times E_k}{m}} = \sqrt{\frac{2 \times 614\,400}{12\,288}} = 10 \text{ m/s}$$

b) The **car** has more kinetic energy — doubling speed increases K.E. by a factor of 4 whereas trebling mass only increases K.E. by a factor of 3.

Q4 a) Distance = work done by brakes / force = 1440 ÷ 200 = **7.2 m**.

b) The temperature of the brakes increases because the kinetic energy of the wheels is transferred to the heat energy of the brakes.

Page 111 — Forces and Elasticity

Q1 a) E.g. if something is elastic it means that when a force is applied it changes its shape and stores the work as elastic potential energy. When the force is removed the elastic object can return to its original shape.

b) The kinetic energy is transferred into the elastic potential energy of the springs around the trampoline as they stretch (as well as a bit of heat and sound energy).

c) i) 600 ÷ 30 = **20 N** per spring

ii) F = k × e
Rearranging gives: k = F ÷ e = 20 ÷ 0.1 = **200 N/m**.

Q2 a) F = k × e
F = 45 × 15 = **675 N**

b) i) The limit of proportionality.

ii) After point P, the bungee cord has exceeded its limit of proportionality. The cord no longer extends proportionally to the force applied to it, so the graph begins to curve.

Pages 112-113 — Power

Q1 rate, energy, watts, joules, one hundred, light/ heat, heat/light

Q2 a) Power = energy ÷ time, P = E ÷ t
(Or equivalent, e.g. E = P × t.)

b) Rearrange the formula to get energy = power × time. The car gets 50 000 × 5 × 60 = **15 000 000 J** of energy (= 15 000 kJ / 15 MJ).

c) Power = energy transferred ÷ time taken = 144 000 ÷ (12 × 60) = **200 W**

Q3 Gravitational potential energy = mass × g × height.

a) i) 46 × 10 × 5 = **2300 J**.

ii) 48 × 10 × 5 = **2400 J**.

b) Power = work done ÷ time
Catherine's power = 2300 ÷ 6.2 = **371 W**.
Sally's power = 2400 ÷ 6.4 = **375 W**.
Sally generated more power.

Q4 a) Time in seconds = 10 × 60 = 600 s.
Energy = power × time = 150 × 600 = **90 000 J** (= 90 kJ).

b) 90 kJ ÷ 30 kJ/ml = **3 ml**.

c) Power = energy ÷ time = 120 000 ÷ (10 × 60) = **200 W**

Q5 a) Josie is carrying her school bag so her total mass is 66 kg. The energy transferred by Josie is the kinetic energy she gains from her acceleration.
K.E = ½ × m × v² = 0.5 × 66 × 8² = 2112 J
Power = energy transferred ÷ time taken = 2112 ÷ 6 = **352 W**

b) Josie puts down her school bag so her total mass is now only 60 kg. This time the energy is the gravitational potential energy she gains going up the stairs.
E_p = m × g × h = 60 × 10 × 5 = 3000 J
P = E ÷ t = 3000 J ÷ 4 = **750 W**

Q6 a) Start 4 – this wasn't a fair test because he slipped.

b) Remembering to ignore start 4 —
average time = **3.2 s**, average speed = **8.0 m/s**.

c) E.g. calculate the power for each start, e.g. for sprint 1 power = (1/2 × 70 × 8²) / 3.2 = 700 W.
Then average these powers. 2804 ÷ 4 = **701 W**.

Page 114 — Momentum and Collisions

Q1 a) If the velocity of a moving object doubles, its **momentum** will double.

b) If you drop a suitcase out of a moving car, the car's momentum will **decrease**.

c) When two objects collide the total momentum **stays the same**.

d) When a force acts on an object its momentum **changes**.

Q2 Truck A's momentum = 30 m/s × 3000 kg = 90 000 kg m/s.
Truck B's momentum = 10 m/s × 4500 kg = 45 000 kg m/s.
Truck C's momentum = 20 m/s × 4000 kg = 80 000 kg m/s.
Truck D's momentum = 15 m/s × 3500 kg = 52 500 kg m/s.
So the order of increasing momentum is: **B, D, C, A.**

Q3 a)

4 m/s	1 m/s
10 kg	30 kg
A	**B**

b) **Before** the collision:
Trolley A's momentum = 10 kg × 4 m/s = 40 kg m/s.
Trolley B's momentum = 30 kg × (–1 m/s) = –30 kg m/s.
(Note the minus sign for trolley B's velocity because it's travelling in the opposite direction to trolley A.)
So total momentum = 40 + (–30) = 10 kg m/s.
After the collision:
The joined trolleys have mass 40 kg and velocity v.
Momentum_before = momentum_after = 10 kg m/s = 40 kg × v
So, v = 10 kg m/s ÷ 40 kg = **+0.25 m/s**.
The '+' sign shows that the joined trolleys travel in the same direction that trolley A was originally moving (i.e. east).

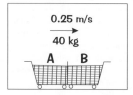

Pages 115-116 — Car Design and Safety

Q1 work, heat, regenerative, reverse, electric generator, chemical, efficient

Q2 a) Kinetic energy.

Physics 2a — Motion, Energy and Electricity

b) The brakes convert the kinetic energy into other forms of energy — mostly heat energy.

Q3 E.g. a roof box will make the car less aerodynamic and will increase the air resistance. The air resistance will therefore equal the driving force at lower speeds and the top speed will be reduced.

Q4 a) E.g. by slowing the car and passengers down over a longer period of time, you spread out the change in momentum and reduce the force that the passengers experience. OR: you decrease the size of the deceleration. This reduces the forces on the car and passengers ($F = ma$), leading to less severe injuries for the passengers.

b) E.g. any two from:
Crumple zones – these crumple in a collision and convert some of the car's kinetic energy into heat and sound energy as it changes shape.
Side impact bars – these direct the kinetic energy of a crash away from the passengers and towards other parts of the car, such as the crumple zones.
Airbags – transfer part of the passenger's kinetic energy to the gas inside the airbag which escapes through pores in the material. (They also prevent the passenger from hitting hard surfaces within the car.)

Q5 a) A seat belt absorbs kinetic energy as the material of the belt stretches.

b) When a car crashes it changes velocity very suddenly. This means that there is a large momentum change which can mean a very large force on the passenger. By slowing down that change in momentum, the seat belt reduces the force on the internal organs, reducing the likelihood of injury.

Q6 Convert time in hours to time in seconds:
1 hour = 60 mins = 60 × 60 s = 3600 s
$P = E \div t = 2\,650\,000\,000 \div 3600 = \textbf{736\,111 W}$ (736 kW)

Page 117 — Static Electricity

Q1 Circled: positive and negative, negative and positive.
Underlined: negative and negative, positive and positive.

Q2 static, insulating, friction, electrons, positive / negative, negative / positive

Q3 a) A polythene rod becomes negatively charged when rubbed with a duster because it **gains** electrons.

b) When a negatively charged object and a positively charged object are brought together, **both** the **objects exert** a force **on each other**.

c) The closer two charged objects are together, the **more** strongly they attract or repel.

d) Electrical charges **can** move very easily through metals.

Q4 Electrons are transferred between the jumper and his hair, leaving his hair electrically charged. Because all the strands of hair have the same charge they repel one another — and stand on end.

Page 118 — Current and Potential Difference

Q1 charge, voltage, work, reduces, decrease

Q2 A — Current — amps
V — Potential Difference — volts
Ω — Resistance — ohms

Q3 a) $Q = I \times t$
$t = 20 \times 60 = 1200$ seconds
$5 \times 1200 = \textbf{6000 C}$

b) $W = V \times Q$
$3 \times 6000 = \textbf{18\,000 J}$ (or **18 kJ**)

Q4

	Lamp A	Lamp B
Current through lamp (A)	2	4
Voltage drop across lamp (V)	3	2
Charge passing in 10 s (C)	20	40
Work done in 10 s (J)	60	80

Q5 a) $Q = I \times t$
$4 \times (7 \times 60) = \textbf{1680 C}$

b) $W = V \times Q$
$9 \times 1680 = \textbf{15\,120 J}$ (or **15.12 kJ**)

Page 119 — Circuits — The Basics

Q1 Cell — Provides the 'push' on the charge.

Variable Resistor — Used to alter the current.

Component — The item you're testing. —

Voltmeter — Measures the voltage. —

Ammeter — Measures the current. —

Q2 circuit, through, across

Q3 a) 1. Battery
2. Thermistor
3. Component / Fixed resistor
4. LDR
5. Switch (closed)
6. Filament Lamp

b) The ammeter must be drawn in series between the battery and the first junction.

c) The voltmeter must be drawn in parallel around the lamp.

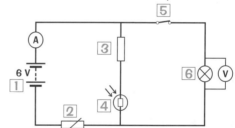

Pages 120-121 — Resistance and $V = I \times R$

Q1 A — Filament lamp
B — Diode
C — Resistor

Q2 a) False
b) True
c) False
d) True
e) True

Q3 a) D
b) Gradient = $4 \div 2 = \textbf{2}$.
c) Resistance = $1 \div$ gradient = $1 \div 2 = \textbf{0.5 }\Omega$.

Q4 The heat energy causes the ions in the bulb's filament to vibrate more. This makes it more difficult for charge-carrying electrons to get through the filament, so the current can't flow as easily — the resistance increases.

Q5

Voltage (V)	Current (A)	Resistance (Ω)
6	2	**3**
8	**4**	2
9	3	3
4	8	**0.5**
2	**0.5**	4
1	0.5	2

Physics 2a — Motion, Energy and Electricity

Q6 a)

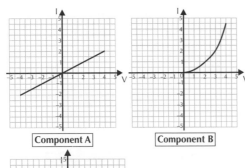

Component A	Component B

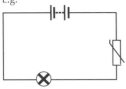

Component C

b) Resistor, diode, filament lamp

Page 122 — Circuit Devices

Q1 vary, thermistor, thermostats, light-dependent, lights

Q2 a) An LED emits light when a current flows through it in the forward direction.

b) LEDs use a much smaller current than other types of lighting (so they are cheaper to use).

Q3 a) E.g.

b) The resistance decreases.

c) The brightness of the lamp decreases.

Pages 123-124 — Series Circuits

Q1 Same everywhere in the circuit — Current.
Shared by all the components — Total potential difference.
The sum of the resistances — Total resistance.
Can be different for each component — Potential difference.

Q2 a) 1. The voltmeter is in series.
2. The ammeter is in parallel with the lamp.
3. The current is shown going the wrong way.
(Answers can be in any order.)

b)

Q3 a) $2 V + 2 V + 2 V = \textbf{6 V}$

b) $V = I \times R$, so total $R = $ total $V \div$ total $I = 6 \div 0.5 = \textbf{12 } \Omega$

c) $R_3 = $ total resistance $- R_1 - R_2 = 12 - 2 - 4 = \textbf{6 } \Omega$

d) $V = I \times R = 0.5 \times 4 = \textbf{2 V}$

Q4 a) The lamps get dimmer as more are added because the voltage is shared out between the lamps.

b) The current gets smaller as more lamps are added. Each lamp adds more resistance which means less current.

Q5 a) E.g.

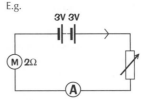

b) It decreases

c) Total resistance = resistance from resistor + resistance from motor = $1\Omega + 2\Omega = 3\Omega$.
$V = I \times R$, so $I = V \div R = 6 \div 3 = \textbf{2A}$.

Pages 125-126 — Parallel Circuits

Q1 a) True
b) True
c) False
d) True

Q2

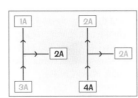

Q3 1. 6 V
2. $4 A - 3 A = \textbf{1 A}$
3. 6 V

Q4 a) Nothing, because each lamp gets its voltage from the battery separately.

b) It increases because the currents to each lamp add up.

c) Nothing happens to the brightness of the other lamps.
(The answers above assume that the internal resistance of the cell is ignored — in practice the current would decrease a little as lamps were added.)

Q5 a) E.g. no, you can have a different current in each branch, but the voltage is always the same.

b) E.g. so that the lights can be switched on and off independently. / So that if one light fails, the others will still light up.

Pages 127-128 — Series and Parallel Circuits — Examples

Q1 Series Circuits
end to end
the same everywhere
shared between components
e.g. Christmas tree lights
Parallel Circuits
side by side
can be different in each branch
the same for each component
e.g. car electrics, household electrics (or any other sensible answer)

Q2 a) If they were wired in parallel, the bulbs would be 230 V because each one would get the full voltage.

b) They don't all go off if one fails / you can tell which one has failed.

c) The bulbs will be designed to work at different voltages. In parallel 230 V bulbs are needed (although in practice transformers are often used to lower the voltage). In series the bulbs used are suitable for smaller voltages e.g. 12 V because the voltage is shared.

Q3 $V_0 = \textbf{12 V}$, $A_1 = \textbf{1 A}$, $V_1 = I \times R = 1 \times 4 = \textbf{4 V}$,
$V_3 = 12 V - 4 V - 2 V = \textbf{6 V}$

Q4 a) i) $I = V \div R = 12 \div 2 = \textbf{6 A}$

ii) $I = V \div R = 12 \div 4 = \textbf{3 A}$

b) i) **12 V**

ii) **12 V**

c) $A_0 = A_2 + A_3 = 3 A + 2 A = \textbf{5 A}$

Physics 2b — Electricity and the Atom

Q5   1. If the engine isn't running the battery might not be able to provide enough current for the fan and lights together at full voltage. So the lights might be slightly dimmer.
2. If the bulbs are in series, taking one out will break the circuit and all the bulbs will go out.
3. The wall lamps are in parallel but they share the same switch.

Pages 129-131 — Mixed Questions — Physics 2a

Q1 a)   Work done = force × distance = 300 × 1500
= **450 000 J** (or 450 kJ).

b)   Acceleration = change in speed ÷ time taken
= 20 ÷ 6.2 = **3.23 m/s²** (to 3 s.f.).

c)   This will reduce the top speed of the car — the air resistance against the car will be increased, and so will equal the maximum driving force at a lower speed.

d)   A seat belt will increase the time over which there is a momentum change, so he will experience a smaller force.

Q2 a) E_p = m × g × h = 12 000 × 34 = **408 000 J** (= 408 kJ).

b)   Two thirds of the potential energy is converted into kinetic energy, so gain in E_k = 408 000 × 2/3
= 272 000 J. Two thirds of the way down, speed =

$$v = \sqrt{\frac{2 \times E_k}{m}} = \sqrt{\frac{2 \times 272\,000}{1200}} = \textbf{21.3 m/s} \ (3 \text{ s.f.})$$

c)   Time = speed ÷ acceleration = 20 ÷ 6.4 = **3.125 s**.

Q3 a)   10 + 5 + 5 = **20 Ω**.

b) i)   I = V ÷ R = 4 ÷ 10 = **0.4 A** (current through 10 Ω resistor is the same as current in all parts of the circuit).

ii)   V = I × R = 0.4 × 20 = **8 V**.

Q4 a)   120 s − 60 s = **60 s** (1 minute).

b)   Train 1 is faster.
Speed = gradient = 50 ÷ 40 = **1.25 m/s**.

c)   E.g. train 1 is decelerating / has a negative acceleration / is slowing down.

Q5 a)   No — the car is not changing speed or direction / not accelerating and so there cannot be a resultant force.

b)   90 km/h = 90 000 ÷ 3600 = 25 m/s.
momentum = m × v = 2100 × 25 = **52 500 kg m/s**

c) i)   E.g. how tired she is / how fast she is driving / whether she had consumed alcohol / whether she had consumed drugs etc.

ii)   F = change in momentum ÷ time = 52 500 ÷ 3.0 = **17 500 N**

Q6 a) i)   4 × 0.5 = **2.0 A**.

ii)   **0 A**

iii)   (4 × 0.5) + (2 × 6.0) = **14.0 A**.

b)   Thermistor — they are a temperature dependent resistor. The resistance of a thermistor decreases as temperature increases and increases as temperature decreases.

Q7 a)   As soon as it's dropped the dummy accelerates under the influence of gravity. So as it falls its velocity increases steadily. When it hits the ground its velocity changes almost instantly to zero and stays at zero.

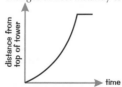 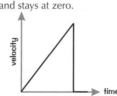

b) i)   Work done = potential energy gained
= m × g × h = 95 × 10 × 60 = **57 000 J** (or 57 kJ).

ii)   Time = work ÷ power = 57 000 ÷ 760 = **75 s**.

c)   Weight of dummy = m × g = 95 × 10 = 950 N
k = F ÷ e = 950 ÷ 5 = **190 N/m**

Q8 a)   her weight / gravity

b)   700 N

c)   There is now a resultant force on her, acting upwards. This accelerates her upwards, reducing her downward velocity.

d)   700 N

Physics 2b — Electricity and the Atom

Page 132 — Mains Electricity

Q1   volts, alternating, a.c., direction, changing, frequency, hertz, batteries, direct, d.c., same

Q2 a)   C

b)   B

c)   A

Q3 a)   2 volts

b)   4 × 10 ms = **40 ms** or **0.04 s**

c)   Frequency = 1 ÷ 0.04 = **25 Hz**

Page 133 — Electricity in the Home

Q1   There should be rings round: cable over cooker, overloaded socket, cable over sink, sockets too near the sink, long cable on the floor, hamster chewing the cable, child sitting on worktop sticking a fork in the socket, lamp that could easily be knocked over.

Q2 a)   Because these materials are electrical insulators.

b)   These materials are electrical conductors, and are used for those parts that the electricity goes through.

c)   Rubber or plastic because they are electrical insulators and are flexible.

Q3 a)   insulation

b)   live

c)   neutral

d)   green and yellow, earth

e)   firmly, bare

f)   outer

Q4   1. The earth wire isn't connected.
2. Bare wires are showing.
3. The neutral and live wires are the wrong way round.

Page 134 — Fuses and Earthing

Q1   The live and neutral wires should normally carry the same current.
A circuit breaker does the same job as a fuse.
A Residual Current Circuit Breaker can be used instead of a fuse and earth wire.
Any metal casing should be connected to the earth wire.
A fuse melts when the current in a fuse wire exceeds the rating of the fuse.

Q2   1. A fault allows the live wire to touch the metal case.
2. A big current flows out through the earth wire.
3. A big surge in current blows the fuse.
4. The device is isolated from the live wire.

Q3 a)   When an RCCB detects a difference in the current between the live and neutral wires it turns off the power by opening a switch.

b)   E.g. any two from: They work much faster than fuses. / They work even for small current changes that might not be large enough to melt a fuse. / They can easily be reset whereas fuses need to be replaced once used.

Q4 a)   **2 A**. (It's nearest to the actual current but still higher so that it won't blow with normal use.)

b)   Because it has an insulated case with no metal parts showing.

c)   two-core cable

d)   They both increase with current size — the bigger the current, the higher the fuse rating needs to be and the thicker the cable needs to be to carry it.

Physics 2b — Electricity and the Atom

Page 135 — Energy and Power in Circuits

Q1 how long, power, energy, time, heat, more
Q2 a) E.g. most of the energy is wasted as heat.
b) E.g. it's more energy efficient (so cheaper to run).
c) E.g. he might think it is more cost effective to buy a cheaper bulb even though the running costs will be more (he may not plan on using the light bulb very much).
Q3 a) 1000 J, light, heat
b) 60 000 J, kinetic, heat, sound
c) 20 000 J, heat
d) 1 200 000 J, heat

Page 136 — Power and Energy Change

Q1 a)

	Lamp A	Lamp B	Lamp C
Voltage (V)	12	3	230
Current (A)	2.5	4	0.1
Power (W)	30	12	23
Energy used in one minute (J)	1800	720	1380

b) A = 3 A, B = 5 A, C = 1 A.
Q2 a) Current = power ÷ voltage = 1500 ÷ 230 = 6.5 A
b) 7 A
Q3

	Drill A	Drill B
Current through drill (A)	2	3
Voltage drop across drill (V)	230	230
Charge passing in 5 s (C)	10	15
Energy transformed in 5 s (J)	2300	3450

Q4 a) $Q = I \times t$
$0.6 \times (12 \times 60) = \textbf{432 C}$
b) $W = V \times Q$
$2 \times 432 = \textbf{864 J}$

Page 137 — Atomic Structure

Q1 a) no
b) ion
c) protons, electrons (in either order)
d) positively
Q2

Particle	Mass	Charge
Proton	1	+1
Neutron	1	0
Electron	very small	−1

Q3 a) i) They fired a beam of alpha particles at thin gold foil.
ii) They expected the positively charged alpha particles to be slightly deflected by the electrons in the plum pudding model.
b) Most of the alpha particles went straight through the foil, but the odd one came straight back at them. This showed that atoms are not like a plum pudding, they have a very small central nucleus with electrons orbiting round it. The nucleus must have a large positive charge, since it repelled the positive alpha particles by large angles. Most of the atom is empty space — the nucleus is tiny compared to the size of the atom.

Page 138 — Atoms and Radiation

Q1 a) False
b) True
c) False
d) False
e) True
Q2 a) i) Background radiation.
ii) E.g. any two from: Nuclear weapon tests. / Nuclear accidents. / Dumped nuclear waste.

b) i) Background radiation is higher in Cornwall due to the type of rock underground.
ii) E.g. any one from: food / cosmic rays / building materials.
iii) Yes. $(1000 \times 0.00001) + 0.008 = 0.018$.

Pages 139 — Ionising Radiation

Q1 Alpha particle — 2 neutrons and 2 protons — the same as a helium nucleus.
Beta particle — An electron from the nucleus.
Gamma radiation — A type of electromagnetic radiation.
Q2

Radiation Type	Ionising power weak/moderate/strong	Charge positive/none/negative	Relative mass no mass/small/large	Penetrating power low/moderate/high	Range in air short/long/very long
alpha	strong	positive	large	low	short
beta	moderate	negative	small	moderate	long
gamma	weak	none	no mass	high	very long

Q3 a) $^{234}_{90}\text{Th} \rightarrow \, ^{234}_{91}\text{Pa} + \, ^{0}_{-1}\text{e}$
b) $^{222}_{86}\text{Rn} \rightarrow \, ^{218}_{84}\text{Po} + \, ^{4}_{2}\alpha$
Q4 1. The particles move in opposite directions — this is because they have opposite charges.
2. The alpha particle is deflected less than the beta particle — this is because alpha particles have a much greater mass than beta particles.

Page 140 — Half-Life

Q1 In 60 years' time, the count rate will be half what it is now.
Q2 a) In 29 years time, the count rate will have halved — half of the radioactive nuclei will have decayed.
b) **125** (87 years is 3 half-lives.)
Q3 After 1 half-life: 720 cpm
After 2 half-lives: 360 cpm
After 3 half-lives: 180 cpm
After 4 half-lives: 90 cpm
After 5 half-lives: 45 cpm
Therefore 5 hours is 5 half-lives.
So 1 half-life = **1 hour**.
Q4 a)

b) There will always be some background radiation (in this case it looks like approx. 100 cpm) AND the radioactivity of the sample will never fall to zero.
c) The background radiation must be subtracted from her readings. The count therefore starts at 640. Half of that is 320 (or 420 including background radiation). This occurs on the 20th minute.

Physics 2b — Electricity and the Atom

Page 141 — Uses of Radiation

Q1
1. The radioactive source emits alpha particles.
2. The air between the electrodes is ionised by the alpha particles.
3. A current flows between the electrodes — the alarm stays off.
4. A fire starts and smoke particles absorb the alpha radiation.
5. The circuit is broken so no current flows.
6. The alarm sounds.

Q2 a) A gamma-emitter with a long half-life is used. Gamma radiation is needed because it is not stopped by air or metal parts of the instruments and can kill the cells of living organisms (e.g. bacteria) on the instruments. A long half-life is needed because the sterilising machine will be in use over many years and replacing the source frequently would be inconvenient.

b) Lead is used to prevent the operator and anyone near the machine from getting too high a dose of radiation.

Q3 a) Technetium-99. It has the shortest half-life.

b) Cobalt-60. It emits gamma radiation, which can penetrate the body and can kill cancer cells. It has a fairly long half-life so the hospital would not need to replace the source too often.

Page 142 — Radioactivity Safety

Q1 a) E.g. he isn't wearing protective gloves. He isn't using tongs to handle the sample. He is pointing the sample directly into the face of the other scientist.

b) E.g. by minimising the time the samples are out of their boxes.

c) In a thick-walled, lead-lined container.

Q2 a) beta and gamma

b) i) alpha radiation

ii) It's highly ionising and can damage or kill cells in our bodies. A high dose can kill lots of cells at once, causing radiation sickness. It can also cause cancer when cells are damaged, mutate and divide uncontrollably.

Page 143 — Nuclear Fission and Fusion

Q1 uranium-235, split, heat, water, steam, turbine, generator, electricity

Q2 E.g. the slow-moving neutron is absorbed by a plutonium nucleus. This plutonium nucleus splits up, forming new lighter elements and spitting out two or three neutrons. One or more of these 'extra' neutrons may then be absorbed by another plutonium nucleus, causing it to split and spit out more neutrons, which may cause other nuclei to split etc.

Q3 E.g. any four from: Fission splits nuclei up, fusion combines nuclei. / Fission reactors use uranium or plutonium, fusion reactors use hydrogen. / Fission produces radioactive waste, fusion produces very little radioactive waste. / Fission reactors already exist, fusion reactors are still being developed. / Fusion requires extremely high temperatures, fission does not.

Q4 **Good points**
E.g. fuel is cheap and plentiful, they produce very little radioactive waste.
Bad points
E.g. no materials can stand the high temperatures needed, it requires a lot of energy to achieve such high temperatures.

Pages 144-145 — The Life Cycle of Stars

Q1 hot, fusion, stable, outwards, inwards, billions

Q2 a) Gravitational attraction pulls the material together.

b) Gas and dust in orbit around a newly formed star may clump together to form masses. The smaller masses are attracted to larger masses, and they eventually merge together to become planets.

Q3 a) A star becomes a red giant when the hydrogen fuel in its core begins to run out. (Hydrogen outside the core is burnt, heating the outer layers and causing the star to expand.)

b) It becomes red because its surface cools.

c) They cool and contract into a white dwarf and then when the light fades completely they become a black dwarf.

Q4 The explosion is called a supernova. The outer layers of dust and gas are thrown out into the universe. This leaves a very dense core known as a neutron star. If the star is big enough this can become a black hole.

Q5
A Clouds of Dust and Gas   B Protostar
C Main Sequence Star   D Red Giant
E White Dwarf   F Black Dwarf
G Red Super Giant   H Supernova
I Neutron Star   J Black Hole

Q6 a) New elements have been formed by fusion in stars.

b) They consume massive amounts of hydrogen.

c) They are formed when a big star explodes in a supernova and are ejected into the universe.

Pages 146-148 — Mixed Questions — Physics 2b

Q1 a) The nucleus of cobalt-60 contains one more neutron than that of cobalt-59.

b) medical tracers — technetium-99m
smoke detectors — americium-241
detecting leaks in pipes — technetium-99m or cobalt-60

c) i) gamma

ii) Because the radiation damages healthy normal cells as well as the cancerous ones.

d) Work out how many half-lives would be needed.
$120 \div 2^5 = 3.75$, so just under 5 half-lives would be needed to bring the count rate down to 4 cpm.
The half-life of americium-241 is 432 years.
$432 \times 5 = 2160$. So roughly **2000 years** would be needed.

e) Any two of: always handle the source with tongs. / Never allow the source to touch his skin. / Hold the source as far away from his body as possible. / Keep the source pointing away from his body. / Avoid looking directly at the source. / Store the source in a lead-lined box and put it away as soon as his experiment is finished.

Q2 a) nuclear fission

b) A neutron hits a uranium nucleus and is absorbed, giving the nucleus too many neutrons to be stable. It then decays into two smaller nuclei and some fast-moving neutrons, which go on to cause other uranium nuclei to undergo fission.

c) The heat from the reactor is used to make steam, which turns a turbine attached to a generator, which produces the electricity.

d) E.g. doesn't produce radioactive waste, there's plenty of hydrogen around to use as fuel.

e) At the moment it takes more power to create the right conditions in a reactor needed for fusion (e.g. high temperature) than the reactor can produce.

f) i) Stars consume huge amounts of hydrogen in nuclear fusion (which creates new elements).

ii) Heat created by nuclear fusion provides an outward pressure to balance the force of gravity pulling everything inwards.

Q3 a) A large current flows through the live wire, passes through the metal case and out down the earth wire. The large current causes the fuse to melt, which cuts off the live supply.

b) i) live, neutral

ii) It doesn't need an earth wire because the case is made of plastic and there are no metal parts exposed or which could touch the case.

Q4 a) A current that always keeps flowing in the same direction.

b) $I = P \div V = 600 \div 230 = 2.6$ (to 2 s.f)
So the fuse needed is a 3 A fuse.

c) The broken plastic casing may expose live parts which could give Kate an electric shock.

d) Time period = 10 ms × 3.5 = 0.01 × 3.5 = 0.035 s
Frequency = 1 ÷ 0.035 = **29 Hz**.

ISBN 978 1 84762 761 2

9 781847 627612

SQHA45